YOU SHOULD SEE MY DOG

Martin Oliver Sami Sweeten

Hippo

Scholastic Children's Books,
Scholastic Publications Ltd,
7-9 Pratt Street, London NW1 0AE, UK

Scholastic Inc.,
555 Broadway, New York, NY 10012-3999, USA

Scholastic Canada Ltd,
123 Newkirk Road, Richmond Hill,
Ontario, Canada L4C 3G5

Ashton Scholastic Pty Ltd,
PO Box 579, Gosford,
New South Wales, Australia

Ashton Scholastic Ltd,
Private Bag 92801, Penrose, Auckland,
New Zealand

First published in the UK by Scholastic Publications Ltd, 1994

ISBN: 0 590 55711 4

Printed and bound in Hong Kong

10 9 8 7 6 5 4 3 2

Hello, I'm Claire and this is my dog. He's called Digby, he's got a waggy tail and I think he's the best dog in the world. He's very friendly and adventurous but sometimes he's a little bit naughty.

We have lots of fun together. Come with us and you'll see for yourself. There are always plenty of funny and unusual things happening in the places we visit. If you keep your eyes peeled you might spot some of them.

Digby loves bones and his favourites have each got a purple ribbon tied around them. There is one hidden on every double page. Look for them carefully – sometimes they are in the strangest places.

Harry's News

The Alley
It was the first day of the Summer holidays. I woke up very early. We had lots of things to do and lots of places to visit. Digby had woken up early too. He has to fetch the newspaper in the mornings.
You should see where Digby gets the newspaper from.

After breakfast Digby and I went to the market. While I was buying some fruit for my picnic, Digby sniffed out his favourite food. **You should see where he found it.**

Chrissie's Clothes-All Sizes
DAVEY JONES

We left the market and headed past a very interesting building site.
Digby decided to join in the digging and hide his breakfast.
You should see where he buried it.

Digby and I made our way to Green Fields Farm. We were nearly there when Digby's sister, Dixie, appeared with the other farm dogs. Digby and Dixie are identical twins. **You should see them both.**

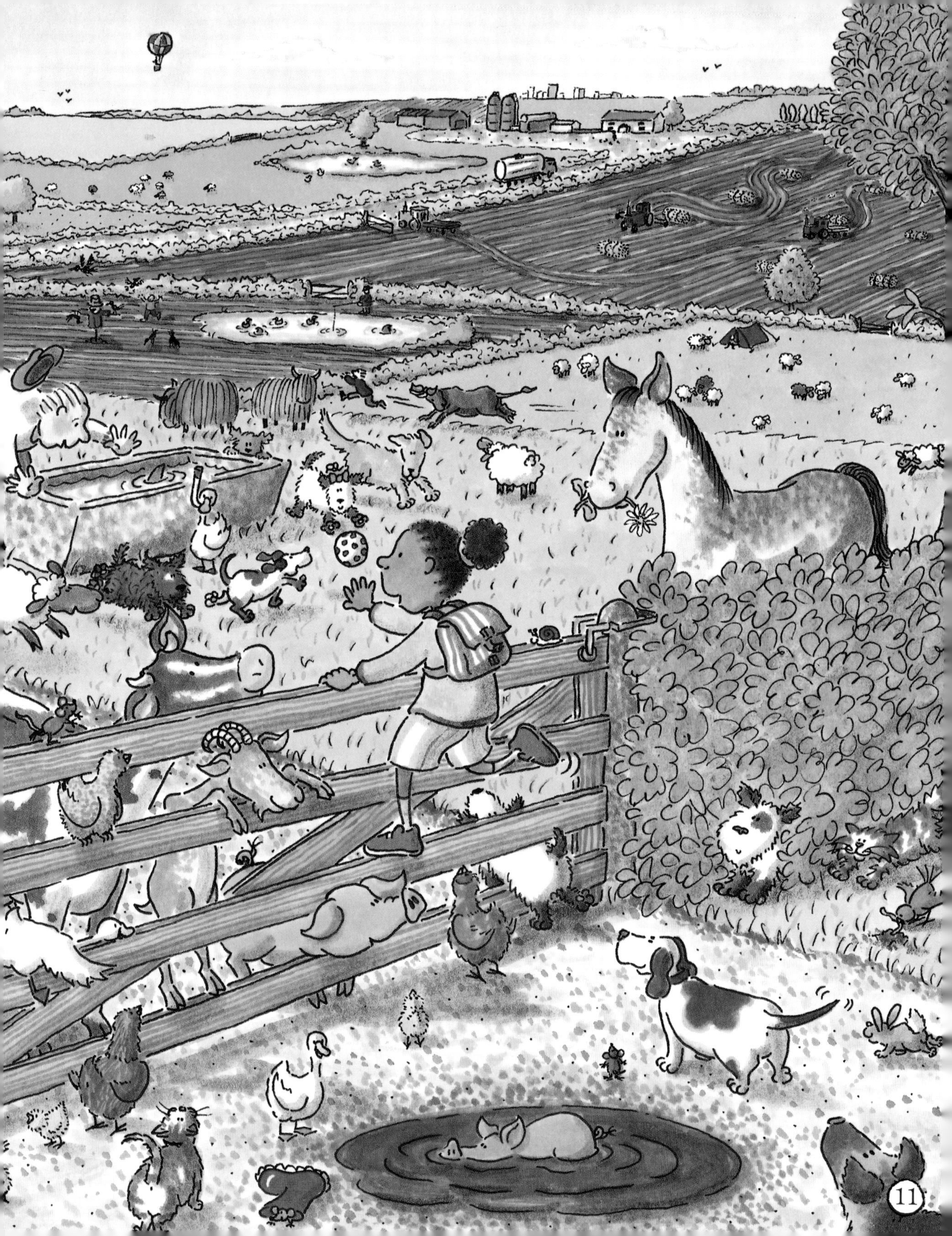

While I helped feed the animals, Digby played hide-and-seek in the muddy farmyard. **You should see where he hid.**

It was almost time to go when I noticed Digby was covered in mud from playing in the farmyard. He needed a good clean, but Digby doesn't like being cleaned.

I gave Digby lots of treats to eat. He was very good but we still made quite a mess. **There are lots of differences between these two pictures. Look closely and you can see the treats I gave him.**

We waved goodbye to Dixie as we left the farm. Before long we reached one of my favourite places. I love to play on the beach and splash about in the sea. **Digby loves the water too, you should see his doggie paddle.**

All too soon it was time to leave. Digby jumped onto dry land and we ran off towards the park. On the way we met Digby's gang. His four best friends are called Scotty, Patch, Lucky and Tiny. **Can you see Digby and his best friends?**

DOG SHOW TODAY
THROW IT AWAY!

By now I was feeling hungry. We left Digby's friends and raced towards the park gates. Once we were inside, I ate my picnic. Digby likes to join in the games in the park. **You should see him playing.**

My picnic was yummy but it didn't last very long! I packed up all my things, then we explored the adventure playground. **You should see Digby in the playground, he thinks he's an old sea dog.**

FLEA CIRCUS
Refreshments
DOG SHOW TODAY
THE FASTEST
THE BEST TRAINED DOG
THE DOG THE JUDGES WOULD MOST LIKE TO TAKE HOME WITH THEM

Just then I heard a clock strike four. It was time for my special surprise – the local dog show. I gave Digby's coat a good brush, then we entered a competition. I was very proud of Digby. **You should see which competition he won.**

KEEP OFF!

Digby won a big rosette and some prize money. On the way back I bought presents for everyone. Soon we were nearly home and I could see Dad picking apples from our tree. Digby and I always race each other from here. I run along the streets but Digby has his own short cut. **You should see the route he takes through the gardens!**

Digby beat me home but I was still in time for tea. Everyone liked their presents, especially Digby.

I hope you enjoyed our exciting day and I hope you can see why Digby is the best dog in the world. **Mind you, if you think Digby is great, you should see my cat!**

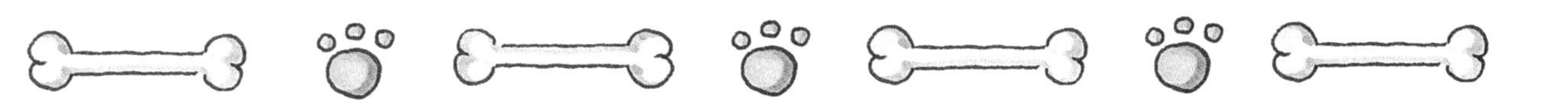

DID YOU SEE..?

PAGES 4/5

Digby is taking a newspaper from the delivery boy here.

Digby has hidden one of his favourite bones here.

Did You See?

Claire
A burglar
A zebra crossing
A pizza delivery dog
A dog taking his owner for a walk

PAGES 6/7

Digby has found a very big bone here.

He has hidden a bone here.

Did You See?

Claire
A friendly dinosaur
Some peckish birds
A wriggly eel
Some wrong-sized clothes

PAGES 8/9

Digby is burying his bone here.

This is where he hid another bone.

Did You See?

Claire
A house with no walls
A vampire with an umbrella
A lady with a wheelbarrow
An archaeologist getting a shock

 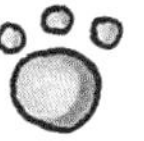     

PAGES 10/11

Here is Digby.

Dixie is playing over here.

Digby's bone is here.

Did You See?
A jumping sheep
A snail on the gate
A duck about to go swimming
A scarecrow
A pig in a puddle

PAGES 12/13

If you follow the trail of muddy footprints from the pig pen, you can see that Digby is hiding here.

His bone is here.

Did You See?
A balancing pig
Dixie
Two hungry goats
A sheep with a scarf
A hen with a big egg

PAGES 14/15

There are lots of differences between the pictures but only some of them show things that can be eaten. The treats that Claire gave Digby are:

A bone
A tin of biscuits
Some fruit
Some chocolate

One of his favourite bones has been hidden here.

Did you see what happened to?

Digby
The oven gloves
The eggs in the basket
The curtains
A picture on the wall

PAGES 16/17

Digby is doggie paddling a canoe.

He has hidden one of his favourite bones here.

Did You See?
Claire
A strange donkey ride
A man trying to put up his deckchair
A surfing dog
Some funny fish

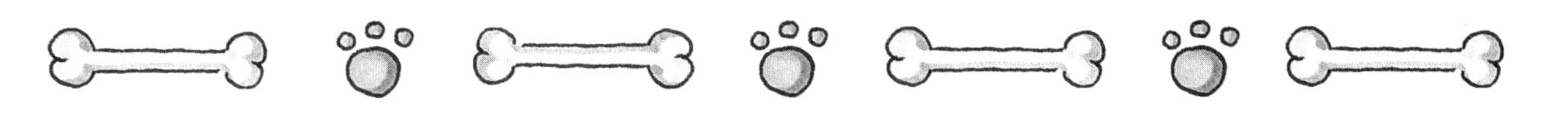

PAGES 18/19

Digby is rooting around over here.

This is Scotty. He always wears a tartan coat.

This is Patch. He has a patch of colour over his eye.

This is Lucky. He has got a bone and a diamond horseshoe on his collar.

This is Tiny. He isn't tiny really, he's very tall.

Digby has a bone hidden here.

Did You See?

A dog chasing his tail
A hot dog
A skate-boarding dog
A poodle
A sheep dog

PAGES 20/21

Digby is playing football over here.

His bone is hidden here.

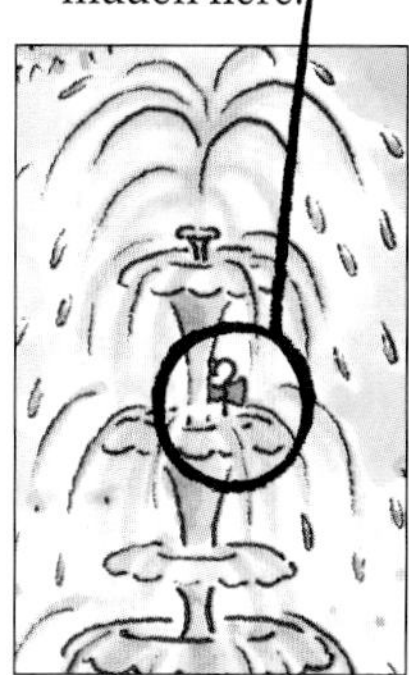

Did You See?

Claire
A jumping dog
A dog statue
A girl flying a kite
A band procession

PAGES 22/23

Digby is being a lookout on the ship here.

One of his favourite bones is here.

Did You See?

Claire
A man walking the plank
A sand pit
A cannon
A red flag

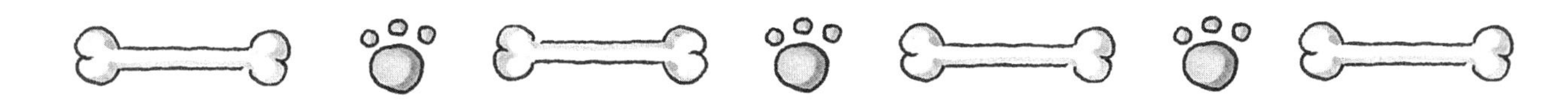

PAGES 24/25

Digby has won first prize in *The Dog the Judges would most like to take Home with them* Competition.

He has hidden one of his favourite bones here.

Did You See?
Claire
Some dogs who look like their owners
A dog training her owner
Some of Digby's friends
A very long dog

PAGE 28

Claire's cat is here.

Claire has Digby's bone.

Did You See?
A picture of Digby that Claire drew
The presents Claire bought for Digby and her parents – they were:
A basket for Digby
A bowl for her mum
A plant for her dad

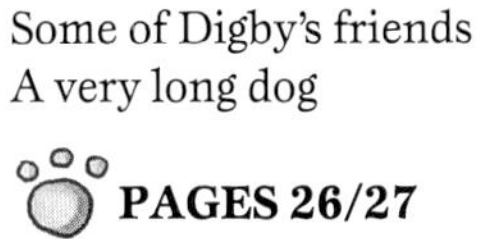

PAGES 26/27

Digby is starting here.

His shortcut through the gardens is marked in red.

His bone is here.

Did You See?
Claire
A tiger
An overgrown garden
A game of football
A man guarding his garden